GRADE BY GRADE
DOUBLE BASS

GRADE **1**

**SELECTED BY
CATHY ELLIOTT**

BOOSEY&HAWKES

Cathy Elliott

Cathy has been at the forefront of teaching young double bassists since the mid-1980s. Many of her students play in the National Children's Orchestras, the National Youth String Orchestra and the National Youth Orchestra of Great Britain. She gained an LRAM from the Royal Academy of Music before going to Cambridge University to study Geography. She then went to Italy to further her double bass studies and graduated from the Santa Cecilia Conservatorio under the guidance of Lucio Buccarella and Franco Petracchi.

Cathy has always loved teaching and a deep commitment to pedagogy developed whilst working with Sheila Nelson on the Tower Hamlets Project. She went on to work extensively training instrumental teachers as Professional Development Co-ordinator for the Guildhall School of Music and Drama and providing opportunities for professional development for string teachers as Chair of the European String Teachers' Association.

Cathy has always had a portfolio career that combines teaching with playing, producing materials for young bass players and working as a consultant for leading examination boards. For twenty years she toured extensively and recorded with the Academy of St Martin in the Fields. She is co-principal bass with the London Mozart Players and a member of the Rambert Orchestra. She is also a regular visitor with the BBC Symphony Orchestra.

Cathy publishes music for young bass players through a small publishing company (Bartholomew Music Publications). She has also worked on many publications for Boosey & Hawkes, including 'The Essential String Method,' which won a Millennium Award. In 2009 Cathy was recognised as a Young Bassists Ambassador by the International Society of Bassists. She was given the ESTA award for Exceptional Services to the European String Teachers' Association in 2014.

Published by Boosey & Hawkes Music Publishers Ltd
Aldwych House
71–91 Aldwych
London
WC2B 4HN

www.boosey.com

© Copyright 2019 by Boosey & Hawkes Music Publishers Ltd

ISMN 979-0-060-13226-1
ISBN 978-1-78454-216-0

Printed by Halstan:
Halstan UK, 2-10 Plantation Road, Amersham, Bucks, HP6 6HJ. United Kingdom
Halstan DE, Weißliliengasse 4, 55116 Mainz. Germany

Piano performance and audio production by Robin Bigwood
Double bass performance by Cathy Elliott
Cover design by RF Design (UK) Limited

With thanks to Aaron, Alice, Annabel, Benji, James, Jess, Jude, Manon, Oscar, Robin and Shiam.

CONTENTS

PERFORMANCE & ACCOMPANIMENT TRACKS

Demonstration and piano accompaniment backing tracks are available for all pieces in this book.

 Track 01 contains tuning notes. Ensure you are in tune with these before using the rest of the audio tracks.

 Demonstration tracks are included for all pieces. Track numbers are shown in black circles.

 Backing tracks are included for all pieces. Track numbers are shown in grey circles.

BACK SCRATCHER

On special occasions (end of term, birthdays, etc) bars 24, 28 and 32 may be played scratching your back with the screw end of the bow.

EDWARD HUWS JONES
(b 1948)

ON THE RIVER

Aim for a smooth ride on the river and let your arm pull and push the bow from one end to the other when you play the three-beat slurs.

HYWEL DAVIES
(b 1962)

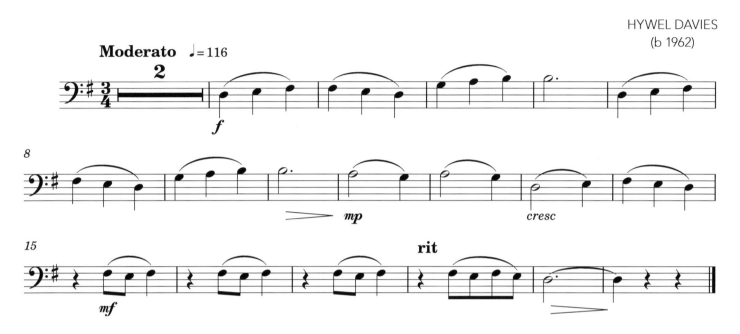

AURAL AWARENESS 1

For each of the following exercises, play the track or listen as your teacher plays the piano.

TASK A - FEEL THE PULSE

As soon as you are able, join in with the music by clapping in time, stressing the strong beats with a louder clap. Is the piece in three time or four time?

TASK B - ECHOES

You will hear a key-chord and starting note, and then a series of two-bar phrases. Between each phrase there will be two bars of silence during which you should sing back the melody you have just heard. Make sure you don't leave a pause, and stay in time with the piano.

TASK C - SPOT THE DIFFERENCE

You will hear a key-chord and tonic, followed by a two-bar phrase. You will hear the phrase twice, and during the second playing one change will be made. Raise your hand when you hear the change. Is it near the beginning or near the end?

TASK D - LISTENING

Listen to the piece and then answer the following questions:
– Where was the quietest part of the piece?
– Was the change in dynamics in the second half of the piece sudden or gradual?
– Was the piece played smoothly or detached? What is the musical term for this?

MUSETTE

A musette was an 18th century instrument like a bagpipe which became associated with a particular form of dance music in France. This musette requires lightly-played crotchets to help it dance along.

MICHEL PIGNOLET DE MONTÉCLAIR
(1667–1737)
arr CATHY ELLIOTT

SCALE SPOT

G major has one sharp – F#. Both **Musette** and **Mama Paquite** are written in the key of **G major** and contain elements of the **G major** scale below. Play the scale with different dynamics.

If you could play the 1st, 3rd and 5th note of this scale at the same time, you would be playing a **G major** chord. If you play those notes one after another it is called a **G major** broken chord. Play this now, and then play the extended version using every G, B and D you know.

Broken chord of **G major**

Extended **G major** broken chord

SIGHT-READING 1

Be a musical detective and look for the clues which tell you how this music will sound:

1. How many beats are in each bar?
2. Count a full bar out loud and then clap the rhythm.
3. What is the key signature and what scale goes with it?
4. What is the character of this piece?

Count a full bar out loud before you begin.

CATHY ELLIOTT

MAMA PAQUITA

This song tells Mama Paquita to buy her baby a papaya and a banana and to go along to the carnival and dance. Stamp your foot in the rests that fall on the first beat of the bar.

Traditional Brazilian melody

A COOL DAY

Feel a sense of calm before you play this piece. Breathe deeply and put the bow on the string in a place that allows the string to vibrate freely. The last note is a harmonic. To play this, touch the D string halfway down using your 3rd finger.

CHRISTOPHER NORTON
(b 1953)

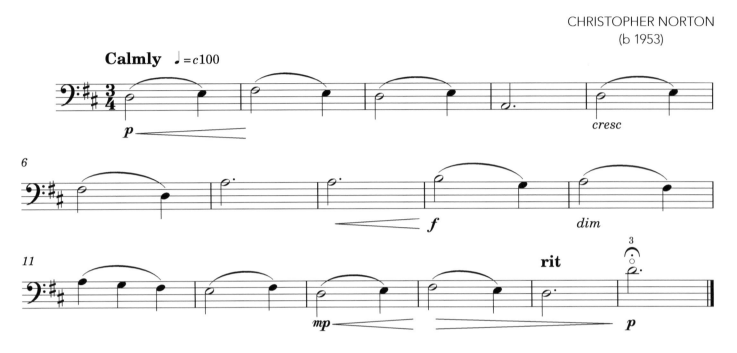

SNAKE BITE

Stamping your foot in the rests really helps to feel them. Rests are silent, but that doesn't mean nothing is happening. When do you think the snake bites?

CHRISTOPHER NORTON
(b 1953)

DARK CAROUSEL

A carousel is a fairground ride where you sit on a wooden horse that goes up and down on a platform that goes round and round. Give your audience a smooth ride when you perform this piece.

COLIN KIRKPATRICK
(b 1942)

IMPROVISE!

Look at the shapes and play what you feel. Use any notes; there is no right or wrong way to play it!

JANET WAY

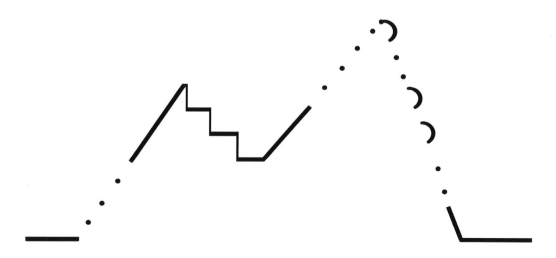

FANFARE (duet)

16 17 18

Play this duet with your teacher or a friend. Swap parts on the repeats so you get to play all the notes. **Maestoso** means majestically. In the 18th century, fanfares were played on trumpets to signal the arrival of an important person, like a king or queen, at a big event.

NICHOLAS CHÉDEVILLE
(1705–1782)
arr CATHY ELLIOTT

CARNIVAL WALTZ

A carnival is a festival with processions, music and dance. Use flying up-bows in the second bar and similar places to give a sense of the dancers whirling down the street having a great time at the party.

CATHY ELLIOTT
(b 1959)

SCALE SPOT

Fanfare and **Carnival Waltz** are written in the key of **D major** which has F♯ and C♯ in its key signature. Play the **D major** scale below with different articulations – *legato, staccato* and accented.

Now play the same scale with the **Carnival Waltz** rhythm (♩ ♩) on each note of the scale. Sometimes start with an up-bow (V) like bar 2, and sometimes with a down-bow (⊓) like bar 26.

Here is another **D major** scale exercise:

Smoothly

CHILLIN'

Put your bow down and enjoy the laid-back swing of Chillin'. Notice the G major scale at the end.

AILBHE McDONAGH
(b 1982)

SIGHT-READING 2

Be a musical detective and look for the clues which tell you how this music will sound:

1. How many beats are in each bar?
2. Count a full bar out loud and then clap the rhythm.
3. What is the key signature and what scale goes with it?
4. What is the character of this piece?

Count a full bar out loud before you begin.

CATHY ELLIOTT

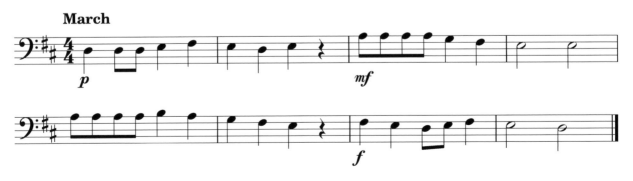

GRADE BY GRADE
DOUBLE BASS

Piano Accompaniment

GRADE **1**

BOOSEY & HAWKES

Published by Boosey & Hawkes Music Publishers Ltd
Aldwych House
71–91 Aldwych
London
WC2B 4HN

www.boosey.com

ISMN 979-0-060-13226-1
ISBN 978-1-78454-216-0

Printed by Halstan:
Halstan UK, 2-10 Plantation Road, Amersham, Bucks, HP6 6HJ. United Kingdom
Halstan DE, Weißliliengasse 4, 55116 Mainz. Germany

Piano performance and audio production by Robin Bigwood
Double bass performance by Cathy Elliott
Cover design by RF Design (UK) Limited

CONTENTS

PERFORMANCE & ACCOMPANIMENT TRACKS

Demonstration and piano accompaniment backing tracks are available for all pieces in this book.

 Track 01 contains tuning notes. Ensure you are in tune with these before using the rest of the audio tracks.

 Demonstration tracks are included for all pieces. Track numbers are shown in black circles.

 Backing tracks are included for all pieces. Track numbers are shown in grey circles.

BACK SCRATCHER

EDWARD HUWS JONES
(b 1948)

ON THE RIVER

HYWEL DAVIES
(b 1962)

MUSETTE

MICHEL PIGNOLET DE MONTÉCLAIR
(1667–1737)
arr CATHY ELLIOTT

MAMA PAQUITA

Traditional Brazilian melody

A COOL DAY

CHRISTOPHER NORTON
(b 1953)

SNAKE BITE

CHRISTOPHER NORTON
(b 1953)

CHILLIN'

AILBHE McDONAGH
(b 1982)

DARK CAROUSEL

COLIN KIRKPATRICK
(b 1942)

CARNIVAL WALTZ

CATHY ELLIOTT
(b 1959)

GOPAK

Traditional Ukrainian melody
arr MARGERY DAWE

poco a poco accelerando

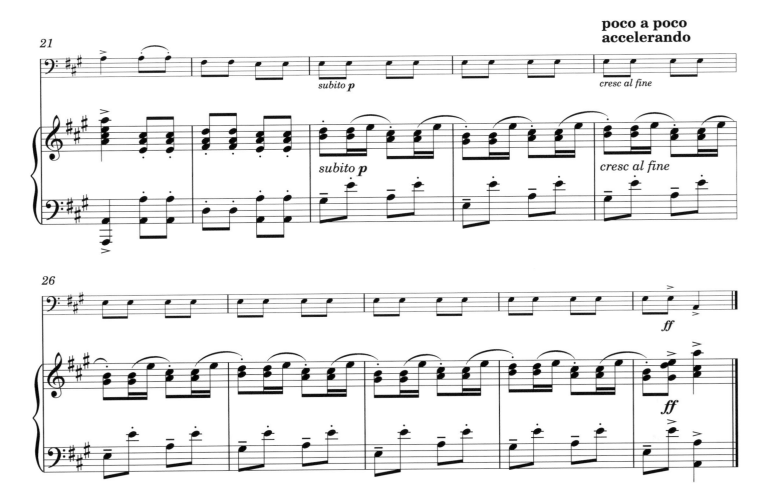

MINUET

LEOPOLD MOZART
(1719-1787)
arr CATHY ELLIOTT

SHAKER MELODY

Traditional American melody

TOODLE–PIP

EDWARD HUWS JONES
(b 1948)

IL EST NÉ, LE DIVIN ENFANT

Traditional French melody
arr EDWARD HUWS JONES

INSECT WEDDING DANCE

CATHY ELLIOTT
(b 1959)
after BÉLA BARTÓK

LITTLE WALTZ

MICHAEL CHRISTIE
(b 1955)

HUNGARIAN CHILDREN'S SONG

HAJDU MILHÁLY
(1909–1990)

Tempo I

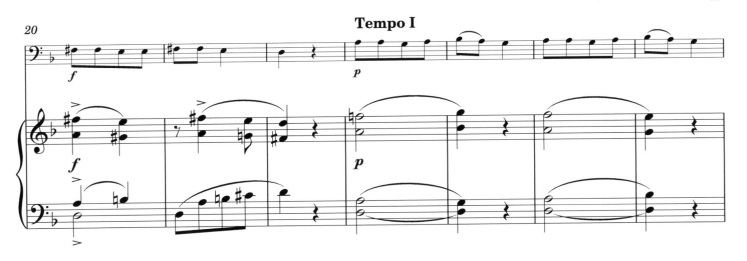

HÉLAS MADAME

attrib HENRY VIII
(1491–1547)
arr CATHY ELLIOTT

AURAL AWARENESS 1 (page 3)

TASK A - FEEL THE PULSE

Ask your student to join in with your piano playing by clapping in time as soon as they are able, stressing the strong beats with a louder clap. Ask your student to identify whether the piece is in three time or four time.
Answer: This piece is in four time.

DMITRI KABALEVSKY

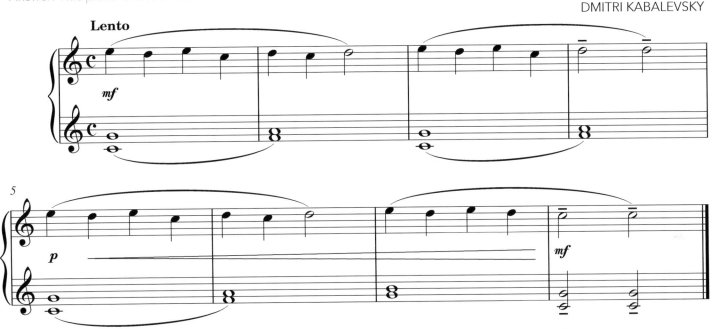

A little tune No 1 from 'Twenty-four little pieces' (op 39) © Copyright 1967 by Boosey & Hawkes Music Publishers Ltd

TASK B - ECHOES

Play the key-chord (C major) and starting note, then count in and play the series of two-bar phrases below. Your student should sing the melody they have just heard during the two bars of silence between each phrase. Ensure they don't leave a pause.

TASK C - SPOT THE DIFFERENCE

Play the the key-chord (C major) and tonic, then count in and play the two two-bar phrases below. Your student should raise their hand when they hear the altered note in the second phrase. Ask your student to identify whether the change was near the beginning or near the end. Answer: The pitch alteration occurs near the beginning.

TASK D - LISTENING

Play the piece used in Task A again and then ask your student the following questions:
– Where was the quietest part of the piece?
– Was the change in dynamics in the second half of the piece sudden or gradual?
– Was the piece played smoothly or detached? What is the musical term for this?
Answer: The piece was quietest in the middle. There was a gradual change in dynamics in the second half of the piece: the music became gradually louder (*crescendo*). It was played smoothly. The musical term for this is *legato*.

AURAL AWARENESS 2 (page 12)

TASK A - FEEL THE PULSE

Ask your student to join in with your piano playing by clapping in time as soon as they are able, stressing the strong beats with a louder clap. Ask your student to identify whether the piece is in three time or four time.
Answer: This piece is in four time.

DMITRI KABALEVSKY

Marching No 3 from 'Twenty-four little pieces' (op 39) © Copyright 1967 by Boosey & Hawkes Music Publishers Ltd

TASK B - ECHOES

Play the key-chord (D minor) and starting note, then count in and play the series of two-bar phrases below. Your student should sing the melody they have just heard during the two bars of silence between each phrase. Ensure they don't leave a pause.

TASK C - SPOT THE DIFFERENCE

Play the the key-chord (D minor) and tonic, then count in and play the two two-bar phrases below. Your student should raise their hand when they hear the altered note in the second phrase. Ask your student to identify whether the change was near the beginning or near the end. Answer: The pitch alteration occurs near the end.

TASK D - LISTENING

Play the piece used in Task A again and then ask your student the following questions:
– Was the music played *forte* or *piano*?
– Were the notes played *legato* or *staccato*?
Answer: The piece was *forte* throughout. Most of the notes were detached (*staccato*) (although some, particularly at the ends of phrases, were held for their full length).

AURAL AWARENESS 3 (page 20)

TASK A - FEEL THE PULSE

Ask your student to join in with your piano playing by clapping in time as soon as they are able, stressing the strong beats with a louder clap. Ask your student to identify whether the piece is in two time or three time. Answer: This piece is in three time.

DMITRI KABALEVSKY

Extract from **A game** No 5 from 'Twenty-four little pieces' (op 39) © Copyright 1967 by Boosey & Hawkes Music Publishers Ltd

TASK B - ECHOES

Play the key-chord (B♭ major) and starting note, then count in and play the series of two-bar phrases below. Your student should sing the melody they have just heard during the two bars of silence between each phrase. Ensure they don't leave a pause.

TASK C - SPOT THE DIFFERENCE

Play the the key-chord (B♭ major) and tonic, then count in and play the two two-bar phrases below. Your student should raise their hand when they hear the altered note in the second phrase. Ask your student to identify whether the change was near the beginning or near the end. Answer: The pitch alteration occurs near the beginning.

TASK D - LISTENING

Play the piece used in Task A again and then ask your student the following questions:
– Does the piece begin *forte* or *piano*? Did it stay the same all the way through?
– Were any changes in dynamics sudden or gradual?
– Was the piece played *legato* or *staccato*?
Answer: The piece started *forte*, but ended *piano*. There was a gradual change in dynamics (*diminuendo*). It was played *staccato*.

NOTES

NOTES

GOPAK

A gopak is a traditional Ukrainian dance with acrobatic jumps for dancers to demonstrate their prowess. The ending gets faster and louder. Start bar 23 super-quietly to have the best chance of making an effective *crescendo* to the end.

Traditional Ukrainian melody
arr MARGERY DAWE

SCALE SPOT

Gopak is in **A major**, which has three sharps – F♯, C♯ and G♯ – in its key signature.
Play four quavers (♩♩♩♩) on every note of the scale.
Sometimes start slowly and get gradually faster (**accelerando**).
Sometimes start quickly and get gradually slower (**rallentando**).

MINUET

Leopold Mozart wrote this Minuet as a piano piece for his daughter Nannerl. Spot the patterns of notes based on the broken chords of G, C, and D majors.

LEOPOLD MOZART
(1719-1787)
arr CATHY ELLIOTT

AURAL AWARENESS 2

For each of the following exercises, play the track or listen as your teacher plays the piano.

TASK A - FEEL THE PULSE

As soon as you are able, join in with the music by clapping in time, stressing the strong beats with a louder clap. Is the piece in three time or four time?

TASK B - ECHOES

You will hear a key-chord and starting note, and then a series of two-bar phrases. Between each phrase there will be two bars of silence during which you should sing back the melody you have just heard. Make sure you don't leave a pause, and stay in time with the piano.

TASK C - SPOT THE DIFFERENCE

You will hear a key-chord and tonic, followed by a two-bar phrase. You will hear the phrase twice, and during the second playing one change will be made. Raise your hand when you hear the change. Is it near the beginning or near the end?

TASK D - LISTENING

Listen to the piece and then answer the following questions:
– Was the music played *forte* or *piano*?
– Were the notes played *legato* or *staccato*?

CORUMBÁ (duet)

'Bossa nova' is a style of Brazilian music developed in the middle of the last century. Play this duet with a teacher or friend, and aim to use the same amount of bow and the same articulation as each other to sound fully synchronised.

PETER WASTALL
(1932-2003)

SHAKER MELODY

Shaker Melody is a dance song written by a member of the Shaker community in America. The lyrics contain instructions about the dance steps telling the participants where and when to turn.

Traditional American melody

SCALE SPOT

Every key signature can indicate both a major and a minor key.

Shaker Melody doesn't have any sharps or flats in the key signature and is in **C major**.

Play this scale of **C major** with separate bows, 2-note slurs or even 4-note slurs:

Toodle Pip doesn't have any sharps or flats in the key signature and is in **A minor**.

Play this scale of **A natural minor** both plucking (**pizz**) and with the bow (**arco**):

C major and **A minor** are related because they share the same key signature.

A minor is the **relative minor** of C major. C major is the **relative major** of A minor.

TOODLE-PIP

'Toodle-Pip' is a fun way of saying goodbye. (As in "I'm off! Toodle-Pip!") Sneak away at the end and then make your audience jump with your final *sfz* note.

EDWARD HUWS JONES
(b 1948)

INSECT WEDDING DANCE

A lively dance follows a gentle introduction. Play the introduction as smoothly as possible to create the mood of a wedding ceremony and watch out for the dynamics in the dance – it is not always loud.

CATHY ELLIOTT
(b 1959)
after BÉLA BARTÓK

IL EST NÉ, LE DIVIN ENFANT

This French Christmas Carol needs contrast between the slightly *staccato* articulation of the first half and the more *legato* second half.

Traditional French melody
arr EDWARD HUWS JONES

SIGHT-READING 3

Be a musical detective and look for the clues which tell you how this music will sound:

1. Count a full bar out loud and then clap the rhythm.
2. What is the key signature and what scale goes with it?
3. What does **Allegro** mean?
4. Is the music played with all the same dynamic? Can you spot the echo?

Count a full bar out loud before you begin.

CATHY ELLIOTT

LITTLE WALTZ

Enjoy the 'oom-cha-cha' feel in the piano part as you play this lovely melody. Aim for a delicate sound at the *p* in bar 21.

MICHAEL CHRISTIE
(b 1955)

HÉLAS MADAME

Hélas Madame is a dance-song. It would have been played while Henry VIII's courtiers performed a lively dance called a **Pavane**. Play it with poise, mindful that it would have been danced at court.

attrib HENRY VIII
(1491–1547)
arr CATHY ELLIOTT

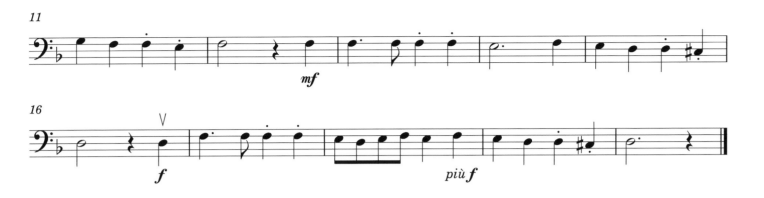

HUNGARIAN CHILDREN'S SONG

Watch out for the speed changes in this song. Experiment with different articulations to help your audience feel the changes of speed and tonality.

HAJDU MILHÁLY
(1909–1990)

AURAL AWARENESS 3

For each of the following exercises, play the track or listen as your teacher plays the piano.

TASK A - FEEL THE PULSE

As soon as you are able, join in with the music by clapping in time, stressing the strong beats with a louder clap. Is the piece in two time or three time?

TASK B - ECHOES

You will hear a key-chord and starting note, and then a series of two-bar phrases. Between each phrase there will be two bars of silence during which you should sing back the melody you have just heard. Make sure you don't leave a pause, and stay in time with the piano.

TASK C - SPOT THE DIFFERENCE

You will hear a key-chord and tonic, followed by a two-bar phrase. You will hear the phrase twice, and during the second playing one change will be made. Raise your hand when you hear the change. Is it near the beginning or near the end?

TASK D - LISTENING

Listen to the piece and then answer the following questions:
– Did the piece begin *forte* or *piano*? Did it stay the same all the way through?
– Were any changes in dynamics sudden or gradual?
– Was the piece played *legato* or *staccato*?

SCALE SPOT

Hélas Madame and **Hungarian Children's Song** (pages 18 & 19) are both in the key of **D minor** which has one flat – Bb – in its key signature. Both pieces have an **accidental** – a note that is not part of the key signature. In **Hélas Madame** the accidental is C# – it helps to establish the minor key.

Play this **D minor** scale exercise:

Calmly

In **Hungarian Children's Song** the accidental is a F# – the third note of the scale. It changes the feel of the music from minor to major. Play the D minor-major exercise below. Decide whether you would like to play it fast or slow, loudly or quietly. Does it feel as if it should be the same all the way through?